DISCLAIMER

Printed in the United States of America
Published by Front Page Publishing
www.frontpagepublishing.com
Available from Amazon.com

First Printing Edition, 2022
ISBN: 978-1-951705-42-8

Transformations
An Anthology

Table of Contents

Dear Readers:

This year, we showcase our new authors, poets, and songwriters as they combine their creative voices in this Anthology titled, "Transformations." Each author is unique in their own voice, as they express their thoughts through the written word.

I am so proud and honored to see their courage and belief in their passion. It has been a joy to witness the process which emulates the transformation of a beautiful butterfly. You will find the heart of the author in their writings.

Enjoy...

Mary D. Welch, President & CEO
Front Page Publishing, LLC

DR. EVA C. BRENT

Dr. Eva C. Brent graduated from Walden University with a doctorate in Human/Social Services with a specialization in Criminal Justice. Prior to obtaining her doctorate, she received her Master's in Psychology with a specialization in Social Psychology from Walden University and her BA in Liberal Arts from Mount St. Mary's University in Los Angeles, CA. Dr. Brent is currently pursuing her dream of being a published author and she enjoys writing short stories. She is a member of Zeta Phi Beta Sorority, Inc., The "Profound" Pi Zeta Zeta Chapter of the Inland Empire. Dr. Brent is a California native and resides in Southern California with her family.

SEEING THE LIGHT
AT THE END OF FAMILY LIES
(A TRUE STORY)

Vivid memories flooded my mind as I received the most distressing news of my life. Memories of my dad placing a rose in my hair in the front yard, my mom cooking her delicious desserts, family vacations to Mississippi, and all those wonderful memories that made me the person I am, slowly faded away into a blur of tears.

Several years ago, I was traveling home on the 60 Freeway in Riverside, California. I remember it was summer and traffic was bumper to bumper. While driving, my sister, Sherry called and I answered thinking it would make the time go by with idle chatter. She spoke no pleasantries, no greetings, just blurted out, "Guess what, you are adopted." I did not believe her and told her to stop playing. Sherry assured me she was serious when she said, "I am not playing. I am at mom's house and the papers are in my hands."

The news was heart-stopping and it was the beginning of the end of my life as I once knew it. I remember a wave of heat and dizziness came over me and it felt like I was going to faint. Now remember, I was in bumper-to-bumper traffic when my life just imploded. I do not recall how I made it home, but what I do know is, that was a transformative moment that changed my life forever.

I cried for months on end and the events that took place after that day changed how I dealt with my "family" and people in general. Sherry and I did not have the best relationship to begin with, but when she told me I was adopted, I wished she'd been kidding.

The secret that was unfurled that day led to a distrust of people, separation from the family and a belief that my childhood was a lie. I felt my entire life has been a lie and was based on a lie. Secrets and lies that families hold on to, do not always remain a secret, and when the truth comes out, no one is prepared for the fallout. I remember hearing comments from various family members saying she's adopted and needs to get over it. No, this is something I cannot get over. Everything I thought I knew, I realize now, I knew nothing at all.

For almost forty-five years, I thought I knew my birth parents, and I had a sister and a brother. Suddenly, I am this floating vessel with no blood ties to anyone. There is a generation of African American families known for taking in a child and claiming it as their own child or a cousin. This was usually done to cover up an illegitimate child in order to protect the mother's reputation, or the child was conceived from an affair. Whatever the reason, it may seem like a good idea at the time, but how does one handle the fallout when the secret is unleashed and a life is destroyed because of those lies? When I found out I was adopted, I was working at a law firm and had unlimited resources to help me find my birth parents. But, all the resources in the world cannot help you mask the pain when you learn you just were not wanted. First, I contacted the County of Los Angeles Department of Children and Family Services and was assigned a social worker to assist with my case. He was very helpful and advised me to contact the Los Angeles Court which I did. I petitioned for my records which I received. I found out the name of the law firm that handled the adoption, only it was no longer in business and the attorney was deceased. I started to realize I will never know my origin.

In the meantime, I asked my mother about the adoption papers and she refused to say a word. She seemed angry that I now know the truth. I supposed I pushed her too far because she yelled, I should be grateful I was adopted because she could have left me in the alley where the dogs could eat me. Those words coming from her were so cold and cruel that it just added to the pain I was already feeling. I shut down and didn't speak to my mother for a long time, but at least I had another piece of the story.

I called my mother's brother, Uncle W. T., and asked if he knew I was adopted. The first thing he did was laugh. This added more pain to my hurt as he stated, "I wondered when you would find out." I called all my aunts, uncles, and cousins and I heard everything from, it is not for me to tell, to they thought I knew.

I called my best friend, Simba who lived across the street from my father's brother in Pasadena. I told her what I had learned and she replied, "You did not know? Your father's brother told me you were adopted when you were a little girl."

My head was spinning at this point. My other bestie always said, they are not your parents, you don't even look like them or anyone in your family. I would laugh and say I look like my father, and I have my mother's hair. In pure distress, I called my bestie and told her my findings. She reminded me, "See I told you!" All I could do at that point was laugh. After I calmed down and had a moment to think, I realized the truth was in front of me all along, but I never saw it. If I had understood my birth certificate, I would have noticed, it was amended. If I had paid attention to the photo albums, I would have noticed there were no baby pictures of me, and if I had listened to the elders talk, I would have heard their whispers. It seemed like everyone knew, except me.

As it turned out, Sherry was also adopted. However, she handled it better than me. I wanted nothing to do with either side of the family because I felt betrayed by everyone. Lies hurt and no matter what the lie is, I feel the truth is always better. As I cut ties with both sides of the family, I remember an uncle who had not seen my children, introduce himself as "Uncle Walter." I quickly addressed the situation by stating the lie stops with me. My children are not related to you and they will address you as Mr. Walter. Well, that did not go well with my father or my mother's family. I tried to explain how I wanted my children to know the truth and there would be no more assumptions about who their cousins were and what those relations were to them. The family argued we are still family. My argument was we are not blood. I told my children, unless a person is from your father's side of the family, they are not related to you. I lived the majority of my life based on a lie and I did not want that for my children.

My medical history was a lie. When I went to the doctor and was asked for my family's history, I told my medical history as I knew it. My mom had diabetes, early hair loss, with a host of other ailments. I was expecting, as I aged, to be plagued with the same type of ailments. Now I know that is not true as I have no idea what my aging process will be like. Now when I complete my medical forms, I write unknown.

For many individuals, they can look at their parents and see what they may look like as they get older. I do not know what I may look like. I look at women of a certain age and I wonder if she could be my mother. I do not think about what my father looks like, but that longing to see my birth mother's face is a feeling I cannot describe. I do not want anyone to think that I did not love my adopted parents. They were my world. They did not have to take me in, they did not have to love me and give me everything they had to make me a success. But, that yearning to know why I was not wanted and what those people looked like and if I have siblings is a longing that will not go away.

On November 18, 1971, I was found in Los Angeles behind an unidentified church wrapped in two blankets. I was admitted to County USC Medical Center where it was determined, I was born on or about November 15, 1971. I was declared a foundling and placed in a foster home until I was adopted, March 1, 1972. The adoption was finalized, June 1, 1973. Sadly, because I was found behind a church with no identifying information, my biological family is unknown. My name at the time was Tonya Termain, and no one was looking for me.

LYNDA DARNELL

A MOTHER'S SACRIFICE

Mama was happy. Happier than I had seen her in a long time. She was pregnant and planning to marry her man, her baby's father. At the young age of eleven years old, the connection between pregnancy and marriage was not clear to me. But one thing for sure, Mama was happy about it. Happy to be marrying, Jessie. She had four children already and desperately needed a man to help her with them. This I learned from overhearing her talk to her girlfriend.

I didn't know Jessie for myself and had no thoughts about him as a stepdad, or Mama's future husband. Her men were off limits to me; no conversations, or interactions, period. The same was meant for them. I heard her say on a few occasions to ever man who came into her life, "Don't talk to my daughter, don't even look at my daughter, unless I am present, and you better not put your hands on her." This was the rule that everyone knew Mama was serious about it.

My instructions were even more detailed. "If any man tries to talk to you or give you anything when I am not there, don't talk to them and don't take it. Just tell them your mother said, you have to talk to her." Mama was especially emphatic when it came to her men putting their hands on me. She said, "If anyone ever puts their hands on you, you better tell me!" She was so emphatic that I promised I would although I really didn't understand what the big deal was. How was putting their hands on me a bad thing? Was something wrong with their hands? Would their hands hurt?

Was something wrong with me? I didn't ponder the issue very much, I just knew if I didn't do what she told me to do, I would be in big trouble. Fortunately, since I was nine years old when the rule was implemented, I never had cause to see what would happen if someone dared to put their hands on me.

Until that day..., Jessie came into my room early in the morning, and sat in a chair next to my bed. He slowly pulled the covers off me and stared at me while I pretended to be asleep. I was very confused. I wasn't afraid, I just didn't know how this fell into Mama's rules. He wasn't talking to me, he didn't give me anything, so I just lay there and pretended to be asleep. Then after what seems like a long time, but could have been only a few minutes, he put his hand on my behind and rubbed me from my behind down to my thigh, just couple of times. Then he put the covers back over me and left the room. I waited to hear the front door close, knowing he was leaving for work. Then I found Mama and told her exactly what happened. She didn't seem upset, she didn't scold me or anything. She just put on her clothes and left the house.

Mama never mentioned the incident to me again, nor I to her. We never saw Jessie again.

FAYETTE FOSTER

Fayette (Fay) Foster is an anointed and inspired woman of God. She is an accomplished musician, choir director and songwriter who has written, produced, and directed four gospel dramas: *Can't Let Go Of His Hand, Don't Wait Until It's Too Late, When The Fear Of God Left The Church On The Side Of The Road, and No More Secrets*. Fayette is also an actress who has starred in several school, church, and stage plays.

Fay was the talent Coordinator for the "For Christ Sake Television Ministry." She then started her own show at the Comcast station in El Cerrito, CA. Fayette is married to Felix Foster and they have adult children. Her future goals include writing Children's and motivational books.

JEALOUSY IS NOT MY ISSUE

I have watched the spirit of jealousy all my life. One thing about the spirit of Jealousy is, people never admit that jealousy is the core issue of their anger, envy, or spiteful nature. Over the years, I've watched mothers, fathers, siblings, co-workers, and church members spiral out of control because of that thing called jealousy.

So, let's define jealousy: A feeling of unhappiness and anger caused by a belief that a loved one might be unfaithful. A feeling of unhappiness caused by wanting what someone else has.

The spirit of jealousy may be driven by low self-esteem or poor self-image. If you don't feel attractive and confident, jealousy can be caused by unrealistic expectations in a relationship. A jealous person usually has the characteristics of envious, covetous, desirous, resentful grudging, begrudging, bitter, malicious, spiteful, green with envy, and green-eyed.

There are two types of jealousy: Reactive jealousy and suspicious jealousy. The root causes of jealousy and envy are connected to a person's inability to see what God has provided in their life and a lack of thankfulness. James 3:16 states, "For where envy and self-seeking exist, confusion and every evil thing are there." Only God can transform your attitude when you shift your focus to one of love, especially when you're filled with GOD'S love.

Growing up in the church, I watched different jealousy scenarios. I started playing piano for the youth choir at my church when I was really young, so I could not sing in that particular choir. Instead, I was allowed to sing in the adult choir. This situation caused a lot of jealousy. Some of the youth asked, "Why is she able to sing in the adult choir and how come I can't sing in the adult choir?" I lost a lot of friends, but I never let that get in the way of enjoying singing with the adults. Never back down just because others suffer with the spirit called jealousy. Never miss your blessings for fear others may not like you if you are blessed to do something others can't do.

Anytime you stop walking in Love, you start walking into a whole lot of stuff and one is Jealousy. Church was one of my greatest foundations and also a place where I saw the spirit of Jealousy raise its big ugly head. People were often jealous of anyone who showed leadership qualities. The attitude was, I can't lead but I'm going to make it hard for you to lead. One of the things that will stop a lot of jealousy is when people begin to walk in love and in their own gift.

I grew up in a household where lack was not an issue. If my parents didn't have it, my grandparents did. I don't remember being jealous of my siblings because I was older and there was really nothing to be jealous of. Even when we got older my grandparents paid for my sister to go to college and paid for her a brand-new car because she needed transportation to get to college. Even then, I don't remember me or my younger sibling being jealous of that. However, over the years, I've seen siblings who grow up in the same household and act like a parent loved or helped another sibling more that than they did them. Here we go with that jealousy spirit rising up. One thing I've seen and know about mothers is that they are very nurturing. A mother knows which one of her children needs more help than the other, and the fact is, all of her children don't need the same type of help.

Your children don't always understand this until they are older. Unfortunately, some children mistake a mother's attention to their sibling as favoritism. These feelings could remain until they are older or have children of their own.

Other scenarios where the spirit of jealousy can rise up is amongst stepchildren, stepfathers and mothers. I've seen stepmothers and stepfathers do everything they could for a stepchild, yet and that spirit of jealousy showed up. The stepchild often feels the stepmom or stepdad has taken the place of their real parent, or their real parents were taken away from them.

This is not always the truth. I understand the concept of families staying together. The main thing is to keep on loving. Letting that spirit of jealousy come in and tear up the whole family cannot be an option. Sorry, but not Sorry! Rebuke that spirit and keep it moving. If you can't get with the flow, then I think it time for you to Go!

As a young adult, I often heard people talk about how jealousy is cruel as the grave. I had no clue I would experience that type of jealousy in my life. When I became a junior in high school, I started dating a young man who appeared to be the nicest guy I had ever met. He would always buy my lunch and if we went on a date, he paid for everything. When he came to my house to visit me, he was always a gentleman around my dad. My dad never allowed me to have company in my bedroom, so we had to sit in the living room with him.

Who would have ever thought I'd experience the Cruel as the Grave Jealousy! In school, I was pretty popular in regards to music. I was a musician for the church and was part of an outside gospel and high school choir. I knew a lot of musicians. During some breaks and lunches, I would meet some of my musician friends to go over some of the music that we would be sharing with the choir. My boyfriend wasn't taking too well to all of the attention he thought I was getting. Day by day, his attitude began to change for the worse. One day he asked me to meet him in the H building at the end of the school day. When I met him, he threw me into the wall and told me not to meet with anymore of my musician friends again. At the time, I agreed to his selfish demands because he was very agitated. My goal was to get away from him and never see him again. I could see this was not going to end good and I could end up getting hurt or killed. That weekend, I shared the incident with a neighborhood friend who told me not to worry, he would talk to him. I was too afraid to tell my dad because I didn't know what he would do. Daddy didn't play with anyone about his children. I don't know what my neighbor said to my boyfriend, but he never said anything else to me again. One of the things I learned from this incident is sometimes people can get so jealous of you, they will try to kill you. Stay away from these types of people.

Now. let's talk about the spirit of jealousy in the work place. Some co-workers have the, "I don't want to be the leader, but I won't let you lead," mentality. Why do jealous people always want to be the boss? Let me tell you this, if they were supposed to be the boss or supervisor, then you they should have applied. If they were not offered the job, obviously their demeanor was suspect, and thank God, management saw something more in the individual they offered the job to.

Jealous people love to control the boss. If they can't control the boss, they make his or her life a living Hell! Sometimes, one jealous person will turn their co-workers against the boss so he will throw up his hands and quit! What an evil wicked spirit! Sometimes co-workers are jealous of that person who will work overtime, so the flow of the office goes well. It's not always about being the boss's favorite, it's sometimes about that person wanting more in their life, and a little extra money, or overtime pay.

Always remember, there are people who work hard every day to make their lives a little easier. Then there are lazy people who get mad at those who take the extra mile to achieve success.

(Why are you Mad?). Always remember, a jealous person has to work that out with God and himself. Jealousy can't be beaten, slapped, or cursed out of a person. All you can do is pray for them, but do not allow their jealousy to fog up your life. If they can't get it together, then they must go. This is not your issue!

DR. ORA ROBINSON

Dr. Robinson is a certified nurse educator (CNE) through the National League of Nursing. She received her BS in nursing and MSN in community mental health at the University of Wisconsin, Milwaukee. She went on to receive her PhD in Human Services at Capella University, MN. She has worked at all levels of higher education starting at the Community College, University level and Post-secondary private institutions, and has held administrative positions as Director of VN nursing program and Assistant Director of BSN program. Her hope is to impact social change within the nursing profession in caring for the well-being of its members.

BLACK NURSES MISSING IN ACTION
"Where They At?"
Why We Stay At The Bedside

There was no Black Registered Nurse (RN), Licensed Vocational Nurse (LVN), nor nursing assistant to be found. For three days, I lay in bed and still, not one Black nurse entered my room. Even though lying on my back was my best choice for comfort, with every movement a sharp pain went to my head. I pressed the call light and requested pain medication. Thirty minutes later, a nurse came in and placed a cup containing the pills on the side table (out of my reach). I'm thinking, this nurse violated the procedure of the six rights of medication administration. I'm thinking, how can I retrieve my medication. A nursing assistant came in and I asked her to pass the cup to me. I still had to lift my head up to take the medication and the pain was excruciating. I wondered why she didn't administer the pain medication via the IV. During this same admission, I was sat up at the bedside to do Activities of Daily Living (ADLs) (head still hurting) and they never came back to help me, "Where the Black Nurses At?"

My sister was diagnosed with cancer, so progressive that the physicians did not know the etiology. Since she smoked cigarettes for years, the obvious origin was the lung. By the time she was diagnosed, the cancer had metastasized throughout her body. Let me share a snapshot of her journey when seeking medical care and the need to have "Black nurses in action, not missing in action." For two years, my sister complained of pain in her back and side. The physicians refused to order any tests that could name the problem, such as a Magnetic Resonance Imagining (MRI) or a Computerized Axial Tomography (CAT) scan. They prescribed exercise and physical therapy, to no avail. After two years she went to a chiropractor who did some adjustments for a couple of weeks. There was no improvement, and the chiropractor (bless his soul) ordered an MRI and found (let me take a pause) the test showed a tumor wrapped/entangled around her spine and her lungs full of cancer. The chiropractor instructed us to go to the hospital from his office. He had already sent the paperwork for the admission and the room was waiting. Tears rolled down my eyes, but my sister was stoic and told me to put them tears back into my eye sockets. She was always caring for me, trying to keep me strong. On the way to the hospital, we made a stop at our older sister's jobsite and shared the news. Immediately, she broke down into tears. As all three of us sobbed, we all cried out, at the same time "Mama."

On her journey these two pivotal things happened. My sister requested pain medication. The nurse returned and administered a medication that my sister normally takes. Before I could ask the nurse the name of the medication, my sister had already swallowed them. As the nurse was leaving the room, I asked her for the name of the medication, and she responded, Lorazepam (Ativan). I replied, she asked for pain medication, not an anxiety pill. The nurse's response was something to the effect, it didn't matter because it would make her drowsy anyway and she would be sleep. No kidding, I can't make this up. That is why (**We stay at the bedside**).

The physician was going to transfer my sister to a nursing home. (I'm wondering why, since the hospice unit was around the hall). When I asked the physician, is there a reason you are not transferring her to the hospice unit? Is it because she is on title 19? (Whatever the #) or because she is black. He was apologetic and said no, no she can be transferred to the hospice unit. When I returned to the hospital after work, my sister had slipped into a coma, and was in the hospice unit (***Why we stay at the bedside***).

A nurse came in and went directly to the IV pump where the morphine was dripping. She did not look at my sister but she immediately increased the rate of the morphine drip. I asked what she was doing. Her response was, she was increasing the morphine. I asked her why she didn't assess my sister's comfort? Otherwise, it looks as if you are killing her. The nurse refused to answer and left the room (***Why we stay at the bedside***).

My youngest sister was diagnosed with lung cancer after several months of spitting up blood. Again, she could not get the needed diagnostic tests to find out why she was spitting up blood. As I type this, I am scratching my head, wondering why they never did a chest x-ray as she was a smoker and always had problems with her lungs. Finally, a chest x-ray was ordered. I remember vividly the day my sister called me and said her lungs were full of spots, all over. She was diagnosed with lung cancer and eventually ended up in hospice. I arrived around midnight and as I entered the room, she looked up and said you came, with tears dropping from her eyes and we embraced. At one time she looked at me and said, "I'm not going to make it am I?" Her eyes closed, and her breathing became labored.

In the meantime, a nurse came in and went straight to the IV pump, made some adjustments with the rate, then turned to me and said, "She should have been dead by now." Wow, Wow and Wow. The nurse continued to perform her tasks with no empathy, no caring, no compassion. (***Why we stay at the bedside***).

My grandmother was in a long-term care facility for safety as she was falling at home and was diagnosed with Alzheimer's (pausing). I was told she was constantly falling out the bed. I contacted the facility to request a bed alarm. I boarded a plane to check on my grandmama. I sat in the chair and watched my grandmamma maneuver her body to raise herself up in the bed. The alarm should have gone off, but it did not. She would turn her body and bring her legs over to the side of the bed and still, the alarm did not go off. As she made the final push to stand up, I repositioned her back in bed. Later, I asked the nurse why didn't the bed alarm go off? Her response was the noise was to too loud and bothersome, so they unplugged it and moved her closer to the nurse's station. (**Why we stay at the bedside**).

My mother was diagnosed with lung cancer, had surgery and recovered nicely. Several months later after complaining of pain in her side, and insisting something was wrong, she was diagnosed with stage IV colon cancer. I'm wondering what happened to stage I, II, and III. Once my mother knew she was sick, I was charged with being there at visits when possible (**Why we stay at the bedside**).

When the visits were about test results, I would usually get a flight to be at the doctor's office with her. When I could not physically be there to accompany her, I would patch in via cell phone so I could hear the conversation. (I was joint health care power of attorney with my sister who lived in town with our mother).

When we received the news from the physician that surgery would not be an option for Mama, because she could die on the table due to the positioning and resultant difficulty breathing, my sisters and I, were with her. She was surrounded by her girls and my brother via phone. This physician was caring, compassionate and empathetic in presenting the news. I remember him touching my mothers' hands patting it and he said, "If you were my mother, I would recommend not having this surgery and to live out the remainder of your life in comfort.

My mother was admitted to the hospital for the last time. She was scheduled to have an incision and drainage (I&D) at the bedside. The physician was on his way to perform the procedure. My mother asked the nurse to assist her to the bathroom because she was unsteady and in pain. The nurse turned and looked at my mama and told her, "No, the doctor will be here shortly," and she kept doing what she was doing. As I raised up from the cot, our eyes met and the nurses face turned various shades of pink. (Why we stay at the bedside). I helped my mother to the bathroom. I heard this same nurse tell another nurse she does not like patient care and that is why she works third shift to have minimal engagement with them. (**Why we stay at the bedside**).

As my mother's condition worsened, the physician made a decision to transfer her to the hospice facility across the street, (does this sound familiar?). My mother was slipping into a coma. Again, I had to step up and ask the physician, is there a reason my mother can't stay in this room and be placed on in-house hospice? (**Why we stay at the bedside**). He wrote the order for in-house hospice and she transitioned in peace.

My daddy was rushed to the emergency room and diagnosed with a urinary tract infection. The physician was livid as this was a preventable death and he refused to send my dad back to hospice. He was admitted and later died, (**Why we stay at the bedside**).

I had a patient who agreed to participate in a research study. After injecting the medications, the patient experienced horrific pain and said he didn't know it would be this bad and wanted to change his mind. The research nurse was called and upon arrival, she started to discuss the patient's need to participate in the study and how he would be helping others. She did not honor his request and breech the main parameter of research. The participant has a right to withdraw from the research at any time (**Why we stay at the bedside**).

The patient's condition deteriorated, and I requested he be transferred to the hospice suite. The patient in the room was here for treatment and not at the end stage of life. Her nurse refused to transfer her to a regular room per protocol. Again, I had to be an advocate and ask my colleague is she refusing to transfer her patient out because he was Black, and the other patient was White, upper middle class, and who was accustomed to getting her way? She turned her back to me, walked away and the room was cleaned (**Why we stay at the bedside**).

Nurses are an extension of the family while the patient is in the hospital. We provide compassion and care regardless of how the patient may behave toward us. We need Black nurses who look like me, my mama, my sister, my niece, my friend and my neighbor. Again, we ask the question?

Black Nurses Missing in Actions "Where they at?"

There needs to be an intentional effort to recruit Black nurses and maintain them. When patients do not see the inclusion of other minority groups and people who look like them, and who can understand their cultural nuances, the patient may not be as committed to follow through on their treatment plan due to lack of trust. Or, could it be the health education they received was not delivered in a way they could understand.

Where are the future Black nurses of America? We are visible if you remove the veil of bias, prejudice and racism. We are here to help you and not harm you. Let us be part of the American dream like immigrant nurses.

TRISHA MONIQUE THOMAS

Trisha Monique Thomas was born in Hayward, CA. and raised in Oakland by parents (Pinkie and James Smith) who adopted her at the age of three. Trisha has four beautiful children whom are her inspiration and encouragers.

Trisha is a graduate from Merritt College (AA degree Early Child Development), Berkeley City College (AA degree American Sign Language) and San Francisco State University (BA degree Liberal Studies).

Trish owns and operates a State Licensed Family Daycare. She is also a licensed Life Insurance Agent and a musician at (Canaan Christian Covenant MBC, Oakland). Her newfound passions are: Designing Bottles and Memory Lamps and Writing. Trish also aspires to become an author and is grateful for this opportunity to share with other aspiring writers.

NO, NOT ME AGAIN

I'm all showered, smelling good, and looking good in my lingerie. I'm blasting songs from my playlist on my phone, and I can't help but feel like running to any open arms to feel safety and warmth. But the only issue is, who am I running to? Who's gonna keep me safe and warm? My kids? No, they are in the mindset, It's all about me. Am I gonna run to my BFF? (laughing), she's in a time zone, two hours ahead of mine and many miles away. I couldn't run to her because at the next block, I'd be out of breath and declaring "Forget this, I'm going back home!" Tonight, I'm feeling lonely, but determined not to get myself down; or to drop another tear. Those who have dropped me like a bad habit have stated that I couldn't meet their needs, and they were too old to wait on me another minute. I'm confused, because they stopped communicating with me on a relationship level two years ago. Oops, did I miss something? Laughing to myself, as I sip on my personal bottle of Chardonnay and being my own comedian tonight. My broken heart has me searching for a place for my broken heart to retreat. Do I hide under covers and close the door to loud children and the hustle and bustle of life? Do I go into crowded places with unfamiliar faces, smile here and there while all along feeling lonely and fighting back tears? Do I risk the strange looks from folks who glance and wonder to themselves, is she ok? Yet they dare not ask.

As my playlist goes from song to song, my heart feels like it's cracking more and more into tiny pieces as I listen to love songs. How can I even phantom romancing and loving the men who swore they wouldn't be like the last one who didn't value me, or who was stupid to let me get away. Well, I guess there's many losers in that club who let me get away. So why should I keep rehearsing the good and bad memories of that one or the other one who walked out of my life and didn't look back; they didn't even care about my roller coaster of emotions or the flood of tears I cried…TRUE! TRUE! They are not coming back and neither is the time and energy I wasted.

The questions consume me: When will I live Happily Ever After? When will my Knight in Shining Armor arrive on his white horse and we ride off into the sunset? When will I get to live out my vows, "…till death do us part," and death be so far from the time we utter "I do?" As I stare into my hand-held mirror, I see my brown eyes glistening with tears threatening to spill over. I don't know if I should cry or yell to release some frustrations. Somehow, I keep quiet, I conjure up my courage, dab my eyes and say, "GIRL, YOU ARE ENOUGH! You are beautiful and you have much to offer to the one who will come along, unmarried, unattached, or uncommitted to another and ready to love you for who you are with all your flaws and shortcomings. He will love ALL of you girl! He will love looking into your beautiful eyes. He will love putting his arms around your waist and choosing not to let go in a scurry to get to his next project or female, as she's demanding his attention or waiting for him to arrive home to fulfill her "honey-do" list. GIRL, why settle? Why continue to discount yourself? Why offer your time, energy, or space to a temporary fix that offers broken promises and unreachable dreams and expectations? As I say to my kids, "You know better"…Huh, I know better as well! How long will I wait for that call that never rings, that visitor who never knocks at the door, the text that's never sent…YOU KNOW BETTER, so When will I allow myself to DO BETTER?"

Now I'm laying across my bed, as the words keep flowing from my head to my pen and paper. As I stare at the white walls with pictures, one of a woman praying and another of an ocean and sky scene. As my eyes go back and forth between these two pictures, I can't shake the feeling of running…Why? Then the answer hits me like a brick, PRAY. Go to that peaceful place by the water under blue skies and pray. These pictures make me reflect on the many times I have gone to the water fronts and sat, cried, and stared into the ripples of the water, as if the answers were gonna jump up out of the water at me. Other times, I'd sit in the car and out of frustration, I'd yell while hitting the steering wheel, or simply walked the long pier silently and with each step I questioned GOD, "Are YOU listening? Do YOU see or even care about what I'm going through?"

Being the "other woman" is not fun for a 50+ woman. Maybe it was all fun and games in my 20s and 30s, but my thoughts now are different. In my 20s, my thinking was, nothing would happen to me. It was fun not having a real commitment. Now, in the 50+ club, my life is more stable. What used to be fun is not fun anymore. My priorities have changed, along with my mindsets and desires.

These songs are making me unmask and face the reality that I'm older, there's no real fun, there's no true love in hiding my actions and feelings…DAMMIT THIS SUCKS!!!! It's hard to say 'goodbye' when I really don't want to. My heart says, "No, don't go," but my will says, "Go and don't look back." I try to block the memories when they start to play in my head. I try to distract myself when I want to make that call. Why is it so hard to let go? WHY? Because you were a dream come true! You showed me love. Love that's actually lust! You met my needs. When you saw something that needed to be done, without complaining or hesitation you took care of it as my hero. You were very dependable, well at least until SHE started popping up and demanding your time. After a year of being together almost every day SHE started interrupting OUR TIME. I tried to ignore it, I tried to occupy myself with busyness, just to fill the time and space apart. But now, one day here or there, has become days at a time that SHE'S taking you from me...How am I to deal? How am I to feel? The real question is...Why am I hurt and upset? Obviously, I asked for this. I knew he was married! I knew his time and days were limited. I KNEW! Did I really think he'd give her up for me? Did I really think we'd have a solid relationship? Did I really think I'd eventually become MRS? YES, I KNEW BETTER!!! Yet, I let my guard down, somewhere along the way. I allowed my emotions to take over. I began to like living in the fantasy of 'my' man coming home from work, eating dinner as a family, hanging out together with the kids until their bedtime. Then the two of us enjoying our time together until we fall asleep in each other's arms. THEN each time we're awakened with reality, and he had to get up and go home to his wife and grown kids. Then night after night I'm alone. So why the tears? WAKE UP OUT OF THAT FANTASY GIRL!!! He only gave you a part of him! He could never give you 100% of him! STOP settling for Satan's tricks! What GOD has for you will last and it won't have any flaws because GOD gives PERFECT gifts. GIRL, CRY YOUR LAST TEAR then do as momma would say, "Go wash your face," and come out looking refreshed and ready to receive the blessings of GOD! YOU GOT THIS QUEEN. CLOSE THAT DOOR! It's a new day, Eyes haven't seen, ears haven't heard, nor has it entered into the heart of man, the things that GOD has prepared for them (Me) that love HIM (1 Corinthians 2:9) This is a TRUE love affair like none other. HIS love and death has covered my sins. NO LONGER will I live in shame. I am forgiven, healed, restored, and soaring in GOD'S love and freedom. I'm CHASING after HIS love and acceptance, HIS validation! There's no GREATER love, nowhere! Because of HIS love, I'm free to be me! I'm free to love and be loved, I am free as a caterpillar larva transformed into a beautiful butterfly. It's time to spread my wings and fly to unknown heights that only GOD can take me. No longer man's girl…I'm GOD'S girl…a child of the most HIGH…I AM WONDERFULLY AND BEAUTIFULLY MADE! I'm never going back to the way it was…NO, NOT ME AGAIN!

DARRELL THOMPSON

Retired U.S. Marine Corps Bachelor of Science Degree, Masters of Science Degree, Century 21 Real Estate Agent, University Adjunct Professor, Financial Coach and Mentor.

THE ONE WHO GOT AWAY

I grew up on the South Side of Chicago, in an area known as Englewood. According to Google, Englewood is known as Chicago's murder capital where more homicides were committed than any other neighborhood in the city. I lived in a dual parent household; however, I was raised by my mom as my father's priorities were work, alcohol and gambling. I considered myself a fairly intelligent kid who did well in school, despite the fights and constant pressure to be represented by a gang affiliation. Walking home from school was always interesting because I had to travel through different territories or gang turfs for several blocks. There were many occasions where I would be chased to school by rival gang members, or I would have to take the longer route with more traffic and adult presence.

At the age of twelve, I was officially drafted into my first gang, the Junior Chi-Town Gangsters. Yes, just like the military, recruits are drafted, however unofficially at a much younger age considering we had to form groups in elementary school in order to protect each other from being jumped during recess and/or walking home from school. Everyone called me Spark, because I have an ear that's noticeably pointed.

Being drafted into a gang was a process whereby current gang members approached you and asked you to represent. Of course, if you represented the wrong gang, there were consequences; such as getting beat down. If you did not have a gang affiliation, you would be drafted and told where to show up for the initiation meeting.

Initiation was not a party welcoming you to the family. It was an opportunity to get beat down by all the current gang members, as many as fifteen or more guys. And, by the way you did not have a choice. If you did not join or show up at the meeting, you would be jumped and constantly looking over your shoulder wondering when. Gangs have changed quite a bit. During my years, we fought to defend our territory and protected other members. Rarely was anyone shot or killed. There were rules of engagement: Harm no elderly, women, or kids under the age of ten. Nowadays, there are no rules or regards for anyone.

I experienced things growing up that would have definitely positioned me a statistic. One of the craziest moments growing up was witnessing my sister, probably in her late twenty's and father being stabbed. I had to be around nine or ten years old. I heard the front door slam open and my sister screaming and running in the house. She was being chased by her estranged husband. She ran into the back room where my father was asleep and dove over the bed. As my father was raising up, my brother-in-law stabbed him in the shoulder, a couple of inches above my dad's heart. He then ran back out before anyone could catch him. It all seemed to happen in warp speed; all I could see is my father trying to chase him, blood over the house. We never saw my brother-in-law again nor was he ever arrested. Both, my father and sister survived, but my father's injuries lead to other life deteriorating factors.

On another occasion, my friend Tony and I stopped to pick up our friend Sharon for school one morning. As we approached the door to her building, we saw what appeared to be a person and scattered groceries near the entryway. As we got closer, we realized it was Sharon's father laying there. He had been shot and killed with a shotgun.

During my High School years, my girlfriend Jeanne, and I brought our son into this world. We were both seventeen at the time. I made a promise to myself and to Jeanne that I would take care of our son and make the best life possible for him, all while trying to maintain my grades and play football. In my junior and senior year, I played running back and linebacker. My High School, Simeon, always had a competitive team.

I knew I was different than a lot of boys my age; I spent many days calculating and coming up with plans to make money. I knew I wanted more than to end up on the street corners of Chicago drinking and gang banging like a lot of the older guys around the neighborhood. I knew I wanted more out of life not for only me but my son as well. Most of the things I did as a kid to make money was, cutting grass, shoveling snow, and I even worked at the neighborhood corner store. I always had that entrepreneur spirit. I held down two jobs; at a gas station with my friend, Monee' and working at Cave Recreation Bowling Center. Due to my work schedule, I eventually and reluctantly gave up football. After school, I headed to the gas station, worked a few hours then headed to the bowling alley until quitting time at two a.m. Again, I was driven because I knew I was destined to be successful and not just another statistic, dead or hanging on the street corner, drinking on the South side of Chicago.

At the Bowling Alley, I started as a porter, cleaning up after the customers. During other times, I watched and learned how to be a pin chaser, the person who reset the pins or retrieved the balls when they got stuck. I was also tutored by the bowling alley mechanics until I learned enough to be promoted to a mechanic.

During my senior year in high school, I dropped out. Dropping out was a tough decision. I know it hurt my mom to the core and it brought a ton of self-guilt and embarrassment to me. However, the demands of schoolwork, sports and working two jobs to support my son became overwhelming. Again, like so many other times, I felt I was destined for more out of life, so I decided to join the United States Marine Corps. I can't remember why I chose the Marine Corps, but I did like that uniform, and I considered myself tough.

I still chuckle at the memory of my mom saying I wasn't going to make it because I was hard head and didn't listen. Since I was underage, seventeen, I needed parental consent to join, and eventually I convinced my mom and dad to support my decision. After meeting with the recruitment officer, I left disappointed that I could not join right away. Unfortunately, I did not meet the Marine Corps weight standards, so I began a rigorous routine to lose twenty pounds. I ran around my block every night and held steadfast to a diet consisting of hotdogs and diet drinks (lol.) Within two short months, I made the weight and was off to boot camp in San Diego, California.

Boot camp was tough for a hard head city boy. I was not used to being yelled at, pushed around, and told what to do. On many occasions, I had to dig deep to maintain my self-control. In San Diego, the bootcamp is next to the San Diego Airport runway. After a long day of training, I would lay in my bed listening to planes take off as tears rolled down my face; wishing I had made a different choice. In the Marine Corps boot camp, its one day at a time; many days and nights I spent praying to make it one more day. The physical fitness was intense, however I persevered and twelve weeks later, I graduated as Marine Corps Private Thompson. I can hardly describe my excitement, knowing I made it out of Chicago, a proud US Marine. Now, the real work was making sure I didn't get sent back.

After boot Camp, I went back home to Chicago and married the mother of my child. Despite the strong advice from my drill Instructors who were against me getting married at that time, my mind was set; this was the girl I had been with since middle school. So, at the ripe old age of eighteen, we got married at the Court House in Chicago. Marriage, as the Drill Instructors described, was tough, but getting married was my way to get my family out of Chicago.

As a young Private in the 80s, pay was not good. My salary was around $558.00 a month of which $179 was spent for food and $139 for living quarters. We got paid every two weeks; on the 15th and 30th. We lived in base housing that was deemed inadequate. Our housing unit, Sterling Homes was built in 1944, and it was outdated and in bad shape.

My early years in the Marine Corps were okay, and I was still adapting to my new environment. My first duty station was Camp Pendleton, California and my job in Radio Communications was to provide command and control communications to the commanders. I enjoyed being a radio operator, however I feared the stories about Radio Operators in combat; whose life expectancy is three seconds because the enemy's goal is to take out the opponents means of communications. Eventually, I went on to a higher-level communication school and became a

Microwave Communications Operator; providing long range communication. Still, it was pretty tough trying to maintain my weight standards, survive with a wife and now our second child, another baby boy. Now with two kids, Antoine, and Brian, and barely living wage paychecks; I made the mistake of trying to uphold that tough Chicago image. I would not listen to people ranked higher than myself. I also intimidated them with threats of fighting, until one day I was pulled aside by Staff Sergeant Johnson who told me I was behaving exactly how people wanted me to behave and that I could be tough all I wanted, it would not help me advance. That talk changed my life. I worked so hard to get out of Chicago, yet I was self-sabotaging my way right back there. This was my first lesson on mindset. You have to change the way you think or you will continue to repeat bad habits. From that day forward, I was determined to change my mindset. Once I did, my attitude changed. I got meritoriously promoted, and was recognized as a hard charger. My name was listed on several other meritorious boards and I graduated #1 in my occupational field. That one conversation with Staff Sergeant Johnson changed my life. I'm grateful he took the time to warn me I was off track. He could have done nothing and allowed administrative disciplinary actions to cut my military stint short. Many times, we are unconsciously looking for someone to care. I know we should want things for ourselves, but in reality, when you know someone cares and believes in you; that can make all the difference in the world.

About eight months in, I received my GED through the Marine Corp's GED program. Just as things were looking up, my mom who taught me so much about life and how to be a man was diagnosed with Cancer. Within three short months, she was gone from my life forever. She was my rock. As a young kid, we spent many days and nights talking about life or singing her favorite R & B Oldies. Her death was a huge blow. After mom passed, my father and I developed a closer relationship. He had a stroke and settled down from the drinking and gambling. We spoke weekly on the phone about life and my business ideas, which he supported. Our relationship continued to grow until he passed.

Life was not a piece of cake. Being married with two kids and broke was definitely not a formula for success, nor was managing finances my strong suit (lol.) I knew how to work hard and make money, but didn't do a very good job at living within my means. It's been said, your knowledge has to keep up with your income level, in order to maintain the income. Looking back, I admit, I felt just because I worked hard, I deserved to treat myself and my family to the finer things in life. Growing up we were not poor, however; many times I was told we couldn't afford certain things. I spent many Christmases and birthdays feeling sad because I didn't get what I wanted. I believe those disappointments shaped my mind to work hard and get everything I wanted. No one taught me the true psychology of money, and the importance of establishing a growth mindset with my money. Since, I was determined to have and give to my family regardless of the cost, living in debt, this mental block landed me into financial difficulties. Day by day, my wife and I, with two shovels, dug deeper and deeper into debt. There were times when we had nothing to eat except beans or hotdogs. Because I was so deep in debt, I often looked for shortcuts, but often dug deeper because of desperation. Many people fall in this trap, trying to hustle their way out of a hole. I know caller ID was invented because of me. I received phone calls daily requesting payment on my bills. I can remember floating (writing a check without having the money to cover it) $3.00 checks, hoping they wouldn't hit until payday.

And, every payday, I was broke because I had already spent my upcoming check with floating personal checks.

Being deep in debt and subjected to the needs of the Marine Corps was traumatic. I had to do two unaccompanied one-year deployments to Japan, without my family. Being in Japan on a military base was like being in the states, however more restrictive with not much to do but workout or drink. During my first tour in Japan, my marriage went through some rough moments. We hung in there for another six years until I began my second deployment in Japan. This time, my marriage ended within four months of my tour. By the time I finished, eight months later, my marriage was beyond reconciliation, and the limited communication in Japan had broken down communication with my sons who were nine and ten years of age. They say separation makes the heart grow fonder, however long separations can also kill a weak marriage. We got together at the young age of thirteen.

Through all my setbacks and roadblocks in life, I have learned many of life's lessons. Some major lessons include: You can't get out of debt with debt, you must break the mental chains of bondage regarding your finances, and mindset is key. Many lessons are passed down through many generations from a place of struggle and fear. We were not taught that money is a tool, and if used the right way you would never have to worry about money again.

While still in Japan, I met my current wife of thirty-two years now. She was also a Marine who was spending her first tour of duty in Japan. Our meeting was a major turning point in my life. Again, I thrived because someone else showed they cared. Imagine being broke, paying child support, housing and living expenses. I had about $60 left over each month. My wife knew what she was getting into even against the odds and advice of all her friends. Still, she took a chance on us. Luckily, she was way better than I was with finances, and seeing I had none, she went out of her way to make sure I was okay, as well as helped me support my sons. This was definitely true love because I had nothing to offer her except love in return.

While in Japan, my wife, then girlfriend, got pregnant with our daughter, Shakita. I was with her until I received orders back to the states. Three months later, she joined me in the states.

During our relationship, we became advocates, helping others with their finances. We enrolled in financial courses as well as college. Fast forwarding to 2022, so much has been accomplished. My wife retired from the Marine Corps with her MBA, and this one time drop out overcame favoritism and racism throughout my Marine Corps career, served in the Desert Shield and Desert Storm War and, retired with 20 years of faithful service. I received my Masters of Science Degree in Cyber Security & Informational Assurance, a College University Adjunct Professor, mentor & coach to hundreds and over 18 years with the Federal Government as a Cyber Security Manager.

My wife and I are in a position to never have to work another day of our lives. We raised two beautiful daughters, Shakita and Keyauna. I was destined to be a statistic with a story that could have read: A Chicago kid with a good heart but couldn't break the chains of his environment ends up dead or in jail. Fortunately, that's not my story because I chose to bet on me when the odds were against me and I appreciate those who didn't give up on me.

So, I leave you with this: Who you become is not based on the environment you grew up in. Your success is determined by your willingness to seek and accept change, make the change and then have the will and desire to persevere against the odds until you take your last breath on this earth. Remember, failure is not the end...It is the half-way point!

ANONYMOUS AUTHOR

WITH NO EXPLANATION

Imagine a once in a lifetime opportunity to start a new chapter of your life. After several years of searching, you've found the perfect location in a fifty-five plus community, with a golf course, tennis and pickle ball courts, two swimming pools and hundreds of clubs to join. You move hundreds of miles from your old rickety home into a new house, so brand new, that you smell the construction dust when you first walk through the front door.

Imagine in this new chapter, you are debt free from a mound of debt that was looming over your life twelve months ago. Aside from the new mortgage, you have no money worries. You're even looking forward to paying the HOA so you can engage in the lingo when the other neighbors complain about the fee increase. Add to this list of firsts, to experience the freedom from that daily obligation, trudging to work for thirty long years, and finally be eligible to receive your monthly pension check. This is the retirement scenario I planned for myself, with the good Lord's blessing. At that time, my current vocabulary lacked the words to express my inner joy. Believe me I tried. I spent hours researching the internet to gain knowledge of new and appropriate words. Suffice it to say, I'm still looking, for the memory when I entered that new chapter of life has never left me. It has only taken me six years to write about it.

Aside from basking in my newfound joy in my new community, I was so beyond grateful that I went out and bought coffee mugs, t-shirts and magnets with various scriptures as reminders so I would never ever forget the gratitude that overflowed my heart. I owed it all to God.

Then how, pray tell, does all that indescribable joy gush down the toilet of disaster in three short months? Did I forget to mention that I started my new chapter with a male companion who I hoped would blossom into the love of my life? I won't go so far as to describe him as tall, dark, wealthy and handsome, but one out of four was acceptable. And, I was not naïve about love. Reality had long ago sunken in about beauty being only skin deep, and the grass ain't always greener on the other side.

Now some "Christian folk" back at my home church might venture to say my relationship with, let's call him Ivan, failed to succeed because we were living in the sins of fornication. And, I'm sure our new friends in our new community speculated the same. However, it should impress you to know that Ivan followed the rules of sexual integrity. During rare moments laced with wine and good food, temptation did arise. However, Ivan started and stuck to the phrase, 'Hold That Thought.' Respect, admiration, and prayed up strength propelled me to follow his lead. And, during Ivan's rare moments of weakness, cause ain't nobody perfect, I dished his phrase right back to him, 'Hold That Thought.'

Admittedly, I am no spring chicken. I have two adult children, five grandchildren and twelve great grands. I've stood before a minister on three separate occasions and promised to uphold vows to death do us part. And so, what I thought would be my last relationship until one of us was called to our heavenly home, was not taken lightly or blindly. Together, Ivan and I had a Plan A and a Plan B. Only thing was, when doom day struck our household, Ivan was supposed to follow the contingency plan; however, he chose to do the exact opposite. Instead of moving on to live near his relatives out of state, Ivan deliberately chose to move to his own apartment, sixteen miles away from me. The biggest infraction was he continued to work in the community of our new home. Early on, he had taken a part time job as a set-up guy for the many events held at the amenity center. When we decided to go our separate ways, he decided to go to work full-time. Yes, full-time in my community. The full ramifications of his employment meant that whenever I wanted to swim, or play my favorite board game, Rummikub, attend musicals, etc., it was inevitable that Ivan and I would see each other. It hurt to hear his voice from around the corner and seconds later run smack into him, face to face. I began to dread the thought that I may even see him with another woman enjoying their retirement years in the same community where we made plans to enjoy ours.

With sixteen months in before we parted ways, Ivan and I had come to know the same people and befriended many. Whereas the decision who to remain friends with would be easy, if only he had moved away like our Plan B stipulated, now it was tough to stand-by while he continued to engage with our friends. His laughter mingling with their laughter caused pain to my ears which began to crush my heart.

Right about this time, I was compelled to confront God. Unlike the song, Have A Little Talk, I'm talking bout some serious talks. "God, I'm confused and unhappy. I don't know how this is going to play out, but I know it would not be Christian of me to slander Ivan's name among his friends. I fear you, God, and I don't want you to withhold any future blessings you have in store for me."

For nine months, I spoke candidly to God. Then one day, a strange peace settled over me and I realized this gated community was not big enough for both Ivan and me. Somehow, I mustered up the courage to do what I believed was the only Christian thing to do. I engaged a realtor to put my three-year old home up for sale, packed my belongings and moved three hours further south. To say my friends pulled every trick in the book to keep me from moving is an understatement. They all pleaded for understanding as to why I was moving away. Questions and more questions were asked and I knew they discussed it behind my back. One questioned another if I had revealed the reason behind my decision to move away, especially after I admitted many times how grateful I was for their friendship. They will forever have a special place in my heart, for they were the new friends that embraced me in my new chapter of life.

If I never found the words to express my inner joy on move-in day, then imagine the pain in my heart on move-out day. The courage I mustered up, suddenly wavered and turned into an avalanche of tears. Off and on the damn broke, obscuring my vision as I drove along I-77 South. Only God's Grace and Mercy guided me safely, as I headed to my new destination.

Funny how your past catches up with you. Two years later, I moved again. This time to the sunshiny, balmy state of Florida. As a writer, I began to network by phone with another writer. Like most people, we began to share bits and pieces of our past. One day, out of the blue, she stated, "Now I know both sides of your story." Needless to say, I was baffled. She went on to clarify that we have a mutual friend from my previous community. A friend among friends who are still wondering, three years later, why I left. As I began to process this information, I decided now was as good a time as any to disclose that it was simply too painful to stay, see Ivan day after day, and realize we would not share my retirement journey together. I also realize it took time to allow the pain to settle within myself, before I could admit to others, the reasons I left with no explanation.

LINDA HURNDON WEBB

Linda Hurndon Webb has been happily married to Jesse Webb for twenty-three years. Linda retired with 36 years of service in the field of education from the Rialto Unified School District. One of her greatest joys is knowing she made a difference in the lives of thousands of students as a counselor, and teacher. Another joy of Linda's is singing, which inspired her to write her song entitled; *Lord, I'm Giving My All to You.* Her parents Jeremiah and Flora, and her brother Floyd all loved to sing gospel. Singing is also a love that she shares with her husband Jesse. Linda has sung with several church choirs and The Perris Singers who won the McDonald Gospel Fest in the 90's, and performed at the Inaugural Ball of President Clinton. Writing songs is a new venture for Linda. It is her way of sharing the gift that God gave her with others.

Lord, I'm Giving My All to You

Ohooooooooooooooooooooooooo

Lord, I'm giving my all to you, for saving my soul I truly thank you.

I could never repay all that you've done for me, I can just live each day in a loving way.

Ohooooooooooooooooooooooooo

May I live my life so that others may see that you reign on high for eternity

Please show me the way as I live each day. I am thankful to you for all that you do.

Ohoooooooooooooooooooooooooooo

You gave your son the only one, your will be done, until you come.

Lord, I'm giving my all, I give it all to you for saving my soul I truly thank you.

Lord, I'm giving my all, I give it all to you for saving my soul I truly thank you.

TRANSFORMATIONS

Poetry

Poetry, also called verse, is a writing that formulates a concentrated imaginative awareness of experience in language chosen and arranged to create a specific emotional response through meaning, sound, and rhythm. - **Merriam-Webster**

Please enjoy the poems submitted by the following Authors as they go deep within to express their feelings and ideals in their own distinctive styles.

Enjoy!

EFFECT
POETRY
MARYd
DR
JGIRL
AZRA

Dollphernea
EFFECTPOETRY
MerryChristmas
ZACKERYLove

Onyx
RIPPLE
possibility
BlackQueen
Presence

MaryD
Afflictions
jGirl
dream

RENEE
AZRA

That's ALL - AFFLICTIONS - FIX the ECONOMY

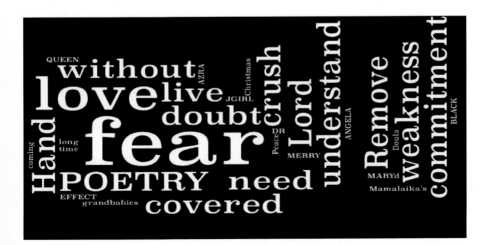

QUEEN
without
AZRA
Christmas
crush
understand
Remove
commitment
weakness
love
live
JGIRL
Lord
BLACK
Hand
doubt
DR
ANGELA
coming
long
time
fear
Peaceful
MERRY
Doula
POETRY need
MARYd
EFFECT
grandbabies
covered
Mamalaika's

AZRA MCCRORY

Azra's journey working with kids started with her love and fulfillment in motherhood, which led her into the field of early childhood development. Azra's background experience in this field cultivated an interest in working with students in diverse programs which included: work with Before/After-School, tutoring, child daycare teacher, the nonprofit sector, curriculum development, and ultimately a unique experience as both an in-home childcare provider and homeschooler! Her love for the youth culminated into a love for educating the Whole child combined with Holistic learning. Azra completed her Bachelors degree in Applied Science, Early Childhood Education. Today, Azra writes children's books, teaches STEM, and continues to develop her business, Wizdom Kids, and the Wholistic Child Care Approach to learning.

OUT OF MY AFFLICTIONS

Out of my afflictions, and after the tears;
You call me by name, You draw me so near.

From the hurt and through the pain, from the struggle
through the storm;
I look to the heavens, and it's me you transform.

Out of your presence, but close to your heart;
You said if I will humble myself to pray, a new thing would
start.

Oh God why me, why do I feel this way?
He said, "In times of trouble you don't want to pray."

I complain, I whine, I even try to hide;
You called me out of the darkness to stay at your side.

Remove this fear Lord, crush any doubt;
It's You that I need, it's You I can't live without.

With my fear and weakness I didn't understand;
With the commitment of Your love, I was covered by Your
Hand.

I call you faithful, mighty and true;
On bended knee, I am running to You.

For Your wings of glory, and Your comfort complete;
I return to the secret place and I lay at Your feet.

Master, Redeemer, Deliverer, and Father;
To go back to the world, I won't even bother.

A heart once battered, and flesh that was torn;
Ignoring your truth, my Spirit would mourn.

But I stand here, not broken, with no stain of sin;
With a smile abroad my face, forgiven again.

In-Love
Azra McCrory

BUILD ME UP

You tore me down, to build me up
You broke my heart, to overfill my cup.

You blessed me, you loved me, you never turned away.
You kept me, you healed me, you gave me a new day.

You extended your mercy, you unleashed your grace.
You brought me to my knees, so I could seek your face.

You gave me your Word, to write on my heart.
You breathed into my body, and gave me a new start.

You gave, you gave, you give, you give
You love, you love, you live, you live

You are the vine, I am the branch
You said I'd bear fruit, you said I'd advance

I heard you, I left you, I stumbled, I fell.
I ignored you, I turned from you; you said I'd prevail.

I doubted you, I ran from you, hiding in the pit.
You called me, you chose me, you were the perfect fit.

I lied, I cried.
I chose my path just to die.
You heard,
Like the dove bird;
And again, you sent your word.

I didn't want to listen, I didn't receive.
With your mighty spirit within me, I had to believe.

I'm in love, I'm renewed, my faith is restored.
I'm intrigued, I'm amazed, I'm not getting bored.

When I walk sometimes I float, but man might not see.
As I look up to you, it's not I, it is we.

You and me in unity, through your covenant we are one.
I am a part of the Holy Trinity from the Father to the Son.

You sent your Holy Spirit, so within me it shall dwell.
You snatched me from the pit, you took me out of hell.

Man has renounced you, man has refused.
You said I'll still love Him, it is you that he'll use.

I love you, I love you, I am finally yours.
Open the windows of heaven that is rains and it pours.

Your thoughts I don't know, your ways aren't fully revealed
But still the land that was barren, now fruit that it yields.

Omnipotent, magnificent, the Great I am.
Alpha and Omega, beginning and end.

DOLLPHERNEA PETERS

Dollphernea (Doll) Peters-Thomas, is a mother of four and grandmother of eleven. Dollphernea was born and raised in Los Angeles. She served in the medical field for forty plus years as a CNA, CHHA, Caregiver, EMT, Firefighter on Palomar Mountain, a Phlebotomist and a Para-Educator for Lake Elsinore School District working with the special needs children of all school ages. Doll served as a volunteer and Ombudsmen on the Navy vessel, USS Dixon AS 37 a submarine tender on Sub Base San Diego. She also served as Navy Relief supervisor, Family Service Center and Navy Officers Wives Club, as well as volunteered in Groton CT working for the American Red Cross.

Doll is excited for the opportunity to present her works in this Transformation Anthology. Her future goal is to write her life's story.

ME …THE BLACK THANG

Me

The Black Thang, moving to and fro' from this place and that
place, never staying for a long time
When will this Merry-go-round stop?

Lay down roots, so we can enjoy our place, so we can make
friends to play with, so we can explore new things,
so we can make memories.

Me

The Black Thang, always moving from this place to that place,
moving to and fro. When will we stop and lay down roots?

Me

The Black Thang, being in a community of Whites, High Yellows,
and Carmels, not being accepted in the neighborhood, pushed
around, not being included in play, teased, beat up because
of my darkness.

Me

The Black Thang, on school grounds, a Caramel skinned boy
leaving his teeth print in my head, blood and tears running down
my dark face.

Me

The Black Thang, calling her names. Am I loved by any, mom, dad, sisters, and brothers?

Me

Am I too dark for them to love? Dad and mom divorcing, dad wanted custody of the Carmel children.

Me

The Black Thing is not loved, am I too dark for dad to love or to see? Unattached to life on earth, please send me to a planet in space, where It's dark like me.

Me

The Black Thang, God will accept me. God said he will not leave me or forsaken me. I feel his presence up here, I feel his love.

Me

The Black Thang, I ask my Heavenly father to forgive those who won't accept my darkness, my blackness. Please forgive their ignorance, their poor treatment of my blackness, those High Yellows, those Whites and Carmel.

Please forgive their teasing, the pain in this black heart. Father don't judge them harshly but save them, those Whites, High Yellows and Carmel.

DR. JOHNNIE SIMMONS

Doctor Reverend Johnnie Simmons was anointed and accepted her call to the ministry in October 1997. She was ordained an itinerant Elder in the African Methodist Episcopal Church in October 2017. She is the Co-Founder and Chief Financial Officer of Sow Ministries, Incorporated where she co-leads a core group of highly intelligent women through conferences, retreats, Bible studies and workshops. She is currently an educator for the Rialto Unified School District. She is also the Director of the Prayer Ministry and the Women's Ministry at St. Paul AME Church in San Bernardino, California.

Johnnie earned a BA in Sociology, a Jurist Doctorate in Law, Master of Arts in Education, a Master of Divinity in Religion, and a Doctorate in Leadership for Educational Justice. In addition, she is a proud veteran of the United States Army Reserves and a member of Delta Sigma Theta Sorority, Incorporated. "Her favorite scripture is; "He that loveth not knoweth not God; for God is love." (1st John 4:8). Johnnie's motto is "Live to give because there is joy in giving."

IN MY PRESENCE

The economy is down.
We cannot get enough pay.
Stop looking around for others to save the day.

This season is not a surprise to me,
But you must remember not to faint.
Trust me during this time of uncertainty.
Don't give up, pray and wait.

Wait on me and watch me work it out for your good.
Put your focus on eternity and don't allow inflation
cause my words to be misunderstood.

This season of the economy did not catch me by surprise.
I knew it was coming and all who doubted me
will watch my true believers definitely rise.

Rise above this financial storm.
I AM still in full control.
My people will not experience repeatable harm.
I AM the protector of your soul.

So my child don't worry about the decrease.
Keep trusting me for the increase.
True faith captures this complete essence.
Trust in me and you will find peace in my presence.

LET ME LOVE YOU
(I)

The tears start to well up in my eyes,
I have really gotten no type of rest.
This situation caught me by surprise,
And I thought you were the best.

The best friend a girl could ever desire,
I have always been there for you.
Now my heart burns with fire,
Wondering how I'm going to make it through.

Through all these bills and all of this pain,
Until death do us part,
Is now feeling strange.
what do I now do with all this pain in my heart?

No communication and our long talks are almost nonexistent.
Long pauses and too many hurdles and deep fences.
You say you want to try and that we are still good,
But it's your actions that are being misunderstood.

You say I am being negative,
When all your words and actions have been repetitive.
I wonder why I still try...
Is it time to kiss this relationship goodbye?

Then I hear this still small voice
That stops me and leaves me no other choice.
I point my ear to the sky to really listen,
I think this time, I might truly catch the vision.

They cannot love you like I do.
Remember, I have and will always be there for you.
I am never fake, I'm always true,
So just relax my child, and let me love you.

LET ME LOVE YOU
(II)

Frustrated, distracted, lonely and no one to care.
I've been there for others this just doesn't seem fair.
I've loved hard and did not ask for much in return.
Now I feel so used and abused, when will I ever learn?

I'm so full of tears and I really don't know what to do.
I hear the Spirit of God saying, "Let Me Love You!"

Still, I dial my best friend and it goes straight to voicemail.
Is she ever available? From the beep I really can't tell.
I've been at everyone else's beck and call.
Now, I need someone's help, and I get nothing at all.

I'm so full of tears and I really don't know what to do.
I hear the Spirit of God saying, "Let me Love You!"

I have given so much, and it was not appreciated.
Talked about and now I feel deeply hated.
Hated for the love that I gave when in doing, I left none for
myself.
Always thinking about others when I should have cared less.

So, the tears keep falling and I just don't know what to do.
I hear the spirit calmly say, stop my child "Let me love you."

WHY WON'T I LET YOU LOVE ME?

I am really tired
of all the ripping and running,
So uninspired
and it seems like everything is gunning.

Gunning for my soul
And especially my heart.
I feel like I am losing control,
And this is not a good start.

So much I have given
And I have not received the same.
This is not really livin'
And am I really to blame?

Always looking for love
And coming up short.
Never raising my hand up above
To hear the real man, exhort.

Always trusting and looking in the wrong places.
Wanting so bad for it to work,
But seeking out all the wrong faces,
And still ending up hurt.

I know how to call on you,
But for some reason I refuse.
Wanting so hard for this to be true,
And forgetting to let you do what you do.

I guess I just don't want to be wrong,
But I think it's time to let things be.
I can still come out strong,
So why won't I let you love me?

RENEE SMITH

(LdyOnyx)

Loura Renee Smith, MBA is married and a retired community advocate. She resides in Southern California. Renee enjoys writing poetry.

ACCOUNTABILITY TO FIX THE ECONOMY

Blood pressure rising
Because of unforeseen
Gasoline and interest rates
Everyone trying to escape or
Recover from homelessness
Living from paycheck to paycheck
Paying high taxes feeling robbed
Many others with no job.

Millions going to the Ukraine.
Not saying it's wrong, but
What about home?

Power outages in Puerto Rico.
Corporate America still
Mistreat you.

When will we show compassion?
Share the resources that keep
Even the basic needs
Like food, housing, and education
Access to medication

It's said we have freedom to
Speak, vote, and carry firearms
To protect ourselves from harm
Maybe you might plead the fifth
To avoid condemning yourself

Where is the accountability?
Who cares for their community?
Don't we all have a responsibility?
In order for all to live truly free
Please tell me how can we fix the economy?

LET ME LOVE YOU [1]
(III)

Salvation is found in no one else
So let me introduce myself.
Let me love you because
I Am that I Am.

Let me love you
Because I am Son of Man.

With Me all things can be possible
Let me love you even with your flaws
I came to redeem you from your broken laws
Let me love you because I can
give you eternal life

You will not perish or be
Snatched from my hand.
Let me love you because
I am your biggest fan.

Because I and the Father
are one in the same,
I hope to keep this very plain.

Let me love you because
I am the only living God.
I know all will turn out fine.

---

[1] As the reply to *LET ME LOVE YOU* by Dr. Johnnie Simmons

Let me love you because
I am God on both heaven and earth.

Let me love you because
My dear child I loved you first.

I have walked on water and
Turned water into wine.
No need to cry with weeping eyes.

MARY D. WELCH

Mary is a retired high school teacher and currently pursuing her passion as an entrepreneur. She is the founder and CEO of Front Page Publishing, LLC. She is an author, screenwriter and editor. She received her bachelor's from the University of California at Riverside and her Masters from Azusa Pacific University. She is a mother of five (5) and grandmother of five (5). As an avid volunteer, Mary currently serves on the Executive Board of the following community organizations: National Council of Negro Women, Inc. (NCNW), The GROUP, National Association for the Advancement of Colored People (NAACP), and she is a Commissioner for the City of Riverside. Mary is now expanding her talents into the filmmaking industry as a Casting Assistant with MegaMind Media. She is happily married to Oliver Welch.

MERRY CHRISTMAS...SAY IT BACK!

Don't be loud, but say it fast!
What do we say Merry Christmas for if no one answers?
Merry Christmas back once more?

Is Christmas really merry?
I think for most folks it is….
Wrapping presents, going to parties, and all that jazz…
Celebrating with family and friends.
Christmas is truly the best time of the year!

Merry Christmas…
say it back, and say it fast not slow.

Cause,
Christmas is one of the best and busiest times of the year I know.

Merry Christmas…
I said it back because Christmas is a special time of the year.
Everyone doesn't say Merry Christmas, but that's ok!!!

You say Merry Christmas anyway!!!

WHAT DOES GOD SMELL LIKE?

God smells like a spring shower.
God smells like an ocean.
God smells like a beautiful rose.

God smells like you.
God smells like me.

God smells like a sunrise.
God smells like the rays of the sun.
God smells like a summer breeze.
God smells like a fresh fallen snow.

God smells like you.
God smells like me.

God smells like fog.
God smells like a baby's breathe.
God smells like a moonlit night.
God smells like a sunset.

God smells like you,
God smells like me.

God smells like peace.
God smells like a tender touch.
God smells like sleep.
God smells like joy.
God smells like love.

God smells like you.
God smells like me.

God smells like happiness.
God smells like goodness.
God smells like truthfulness.

God smells like you.
God smells like me.

God smells like a lake.
God smells like kindness.
God smells like thoughtfulness.
God smells like prayers on our knees.

God smells like you and God smells like me.
God smells like you and God smells like me.

I THINK IT'S BY DESIGN

No one can see what you think, and
No one can read your mind.
Your thoughts are private
Near and dear to you alone,
I think it's by design.

You never have to make your thoughts known.
You never have to say it aloud.
What do you feel?
What do you think?
Only you know, what's true for you.
I think it's by design.

THAT'S IT ... THAT'S ALL!

Some people are short and others are tall.
That's it... that's all!

Some animals are big and others are small.
That's it... that's all!

Some can jump and others can crawl.
That's it...that's all!

Some birds can swim and some can fly.
That's it...that's all!

Sometimes it rains and sometimes it snows.
That's it... that's all!

Sometimes it's hot and sometimes it's cold.
That's it...that's all!

Sometimes we need a lollipop!
That's it.,.that's all!

Ice Cream may take your problems away...
Temporarily anyway!
That's it...that's all!
That's it...that's all!!

THE PAST

Is it too much to ask to remember the past?
To never forget the love and the sounds of life and
people all around.
The good times are what we tend to review.
But the bad times need remembering too!

The people who came before us would probably agree.
Keep the love for one another at the forefront of thee.
The Past can never be changed or altered...we can learn
from the past how not to falter.

We can always look back and see where we have come from.
Measuring, judging, and comparing the past to,
where we are now and how we grew.

Our past is not one incident, not one moment in time.
Our past is rich with people and life is so divine.
We are not one-dimensional you see!
We are all the products of our past, you and me!

IN LOVING MEMORY OF
BLAKE LEE ZACKERY

SUBMITTED BY MOTHER
DR. ADRIENNE ZACKERY

RIPPLE EFFECT

I looked at myself and my image changed,
As I encountered the feel of crippling pain.
Wishing it be my goat to scape, would be my excuse to blame.
As I looked around realizing my surroundings, I stood stuck in pain
Weighted by regrets, I looked down in shame.
On my neck it felt wet, effects from the storm that came.
Drowned in sorrow, I swore to take responsibility, to never put on that mask, nor perform that way.
I wipe away tears, the definition of INSANE, roared in brain.
Again, and again and again, I expect the sore to wane,
Instead, it gets worse, caused by the agony brought forth this day.
Shackled to the past-present-future, heinous and horrid play,
Motions and maneuvers that are ingrained on strains, in non-morbid DNA.
Somehow, I feel that mistakes, I was born to make.
When I gave up on wiping away tears which gave me a horrid face.
They dropped onto the blacktop as accumulated with drops from black clouds that allowed me to see my image, my glimpse in space, of who I am as my portrait changed.
Who or what I was seconds ago, had grown in age.
Centuries, like scars are sketched on my skin,
From centuries and scares it has felt like, stored in cage.
Where broken beast, who are hurt and feast on feelings, engorged in hate.
My image flickers still, while I endure the pain,
Until the pour plays out, then I cease to falter, my vision clears, victory appears to some who remain themselves, until the sun comes out and soars with rays.

That helps paint my imperfect picture, which shows that even as my image changed, there was no diminished faith, what I saw in the stressful shower, was just the means of grace.

A sign like lines I the road, tells one to keep up pace.

"Don't worry what you look like, what matters is for you to finish the race."

Make it to the shade.

What was once imagined is now a reality.

A mirror, my reflection in a peaceful place.

The calm came upon waters that rippled,

Which caused so many forms to change.

Now at seasons end, I've come to know I was born to reign,

And watch who I was to become, who I am today.

Who Else But Blake...

Coming Soon:
Reflections an Anthology

Front Page Publishing is accepting stories, poems, songs, and speeches for the next anthology. We invite all new authors to accept this opportunity to debut your literary projects.

For updated information on submissions, log onto Frontpagepublishing.com.

Made in the USA
Monee, IL
04 March 2023

28585226R00059